A-Zenith of Creatures

by ANGIE RAIFF and GREG CHINLUND
illustrated by LIZ RAIFF

Bear Lake Publishing

Text copyright © 1995 by Angie Raiff and Greg Chinlund
Illustrations copyright © 1997 by Liz Raiff

The text was set in 36/43-point Palatino

All rights reserved. Published 1997.
Printed in Mexico.
01 00 99 98   4 3 2

Library of Congress Catalog Card Number: 97–92688

ISBN 0-9661132-0-9

Note to Parents and Teachers:
As you read, try to find
each letter hidden within,
but as you do, please keep in mind
their eyes and their grin.

"A" is for alligator living in a swamp.

"B" is for beaver building his home
with a chomp.

"C" is for canary singing a sweet song.

"D" is for dolphin swimming along.

"E" is for eagle soaring high in the sky.

"F" is for frog catching a fly.

"G" is for gopher
living underground.

"H" is for hyena making a laughing sound.

"I" is for iguana living in the heat.

"J" is for jack rabbit *fast* on his feet.

"K" is kangaroo hopping all around.

"L" is for lion romping on the ground.

"M" is for monkey
swinging hand over hand.

"N" is for newt leaving tracks in the sand.

"O" is for octopus spraying its ink.

"P" is for pig with an awful *stink*!

"Q" is for quail flying away.

"R" is for reindeer on a snowy winter day.

"S" is for shark lurking in the *deep*.

"T" is for tarantula giving you the *creeps*.

"U" is for unicorn a white horse with a horn.

"V" is for vulture, hunting while airborne.

"W" is for wolf, in packs are so **bold!**

"X" is for xeme living in the cold.

"Y" is for yak not afraid of heights.

"Z" is for zebra full of stripes.

Interesting facts . . . keep reading!

Alligators and crocodiles are two different animals, although they look alike. The alligator's body is suited for life on land and in the water. Most alligators in the United States are found living in the waters and lowlands of the Southeastern states.

Beavers are small furry creatures that eat bark and use the branches to build dams and lodges (homes) in the water. Beavers live in streams, rivers, and freshwater lakes near woodlands. There are more beavers in the United States and Canada than anywhere else in the world.

Canaries are one of the most popular pet birds. These bright yellow birds are bred in captivity for their beautiful songs. A tame canary ranges in color from pale yellow to bright yellow. A wild canary has dark green and olive colored markings. Canaries live and nest in small bushes and trees.

Dolphins are mammals, not fish. They have lungs and are warm-blooded, just like us. These mammals swim free in most of the oceans of the world. Many dolphins remain near land living in shallow bays and protected inlets.

Eagles are one of the largest and most powerful birds in the world. The eagle soars gracefully high in the air. In 1782 the bald eagle was chosen as the national bird of the United States. These beautiful creatures survive everywhere throughout the world except in Antarctica and live mainly near rivers and lakes. Eagles nest in tall trees and on cliffs.

Frogs are small tailless animals with bulging eyes. They are found living on every continent except Antarctica. Most species of frogs are found in tropical regions. This animal spends part of its life as a water animal and part as a land animal.

Gophers are small mammals that live in long, underground tunnels. They spend most of their time alone in these dark tunnels that may be as long as 800 feet. Gophers live in all regions in North America. Gophers are commonly found in grassy or slightly wooded areas.

Hyenas are mammals that have become popular in cartoons. They are know for their crazy howl, which sounds like a strange human laugh. There are several kinds of hyenas: spotted (also known as laughing), striped, and brown. Hyenas are indigenous to Africa living on the open, grassy plains.

Iguanas live in deserts or other dry habitats, but a few species live in tropical rain forests. Green iguanas live in trees, especially near water. The marine iguana is the only lizard that lives in the sea. The land iguana never goes near water. Iguanas can be found in North, Central, and South America.

Jack rabbits are special rabbits that have long hind legs, large eyes, and long ears. This large hare is found in the deserts and on prairies. Most jack rabbits live in western North America.

Kangaroos are fur covered mammals that hop on their hind legs. Kangaroo mothers carry their young in a pouch. These creatures are found living in the grasslands of Australia.

Lions, often called the "King of Beasts," are large, powerful cats. Lions live in woodlands, grassy plains, and areas with thorny scrub trees. These great animals are found in Africa and India.

Monkeys are primates that have flat, rather human-like faces. Contrary to popular belief, monkeys rarely swing on vines; but rather run along branches on all fours. Monkeys are found in tropical and subtropical climates.

Newts are small, slender, often brightly colored salamanders. These creatures live chiefly on the land, but become aquatic in order to reproduce. Newts live near water in wooded areas.

Octopuses are sea animals. The best-known species live on rocky, sandy, or muddy bottoms in shallow parts of the oceans throughout the world. Other octopuses live in deep waters.

Pigs, also called swine or hogs, are domesticated animals with a long snout and a thick, fat body cover. These creatures are commonly pictured as living on farms in muddy fenced areas.

Quails are small birds that live on every continent except Antarctica. Out of the 45 species of quail, about 20 of them are found in North America. Most of the quail in the United States are found in the Western and Southwestern states. These creatures live in the foothills and valleys of mountainous regions.

Reindeer are large migrating deer that live in the northernmost regions of Europe, Asia, and North America. Reindeer that live in North America are called caribou. These animals are very powerful and can travel 40 miles a day while pulling twice their own weight. Reindeer are most commonly found in the arctic tundra. Amazingly, these large animals are excellent swimmers.

Sharks are predatory fish that live in all seas around the world, but are most abundant in warmer waters. Most sharks do not attack humans as the movies would have us believe.

Tarantulas are a type of spider that live in warm climates, such as those of the southern and western United States and tropics. Tarantulas found in the United States are quiet creatures that live in burrows.

Unicorns are animals which are described in fables. The unicorn is a white horse with a long, straight spiraled horn extending from the middle of its forehead. This creature was said to be native to India.

Vultures, also known as buzzards, are large birds of prey that live on all continents except Australia and Antarctica, usually in open country. Vultures tend to live alone, but feed in groups.

Wolves are one of the largest members of the dog family. They can live in almost any climate, though they are usually not found in deserts or tropical forests. These creatures are typically found in wooded and rugged areas of North America.

Xemes are gulls that survive in the Arctic. It is also known as the fork-tailed gull. These birds have long, narrow wings adapted for soaring.

Yaks are a wild ox found primarily in the mountains of central Asia. These shaggy-haired animals live in small isolated herds at elevations sometimes over 14,000 feet.

Zebras are striped, horselike animals found living in the wild on the grassy plains of Africa. These amazing creatures may also live in captivity at a local zoo. The zebra has alternating white and black or brown stripes as its unique markings.

Did *you* find the hidden letters?

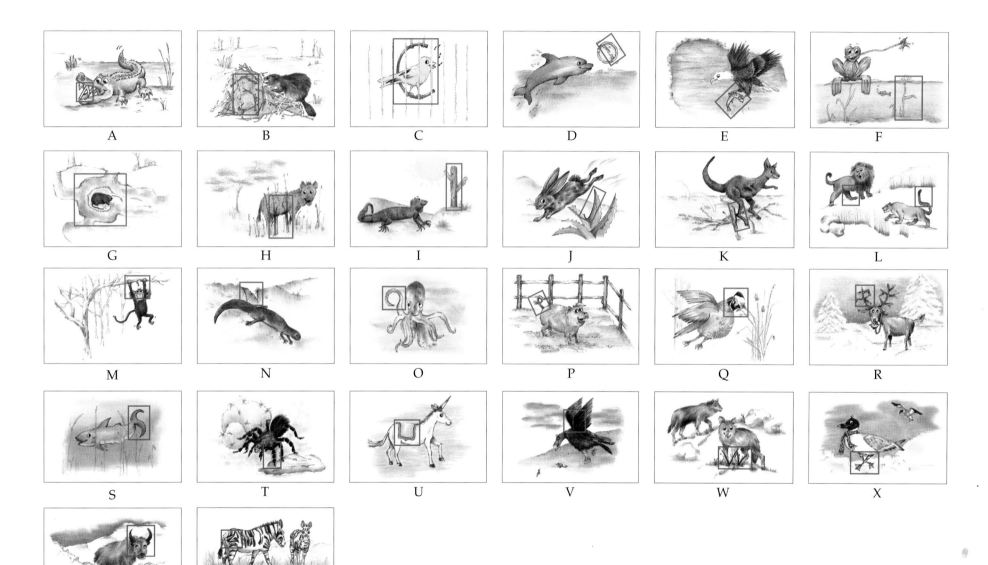